a book of poetry written by
Lauren Richmond

Peoples Education
Your partner in student success

299 Market Street
Saddle Brook, NJ 07663
800-822-1080
PeoplesEducation.com

ISBN 978-1-4138-8548-4

Printed in the United States of America.

10 9 8 7 6 5 4 3 2 1

About the Title

At every preschool, including the one I attended, the little students always get "free" or play time and I tended to spend all of my time drawing at the easel. All of my artistic creations had one common thread; they were all drawn with black and brown markers and only black and brown markers.

Now I can promise you that there was no hidden message within my color choices. I can assure you that at the time those were the colors that appealed to me. However, my teachers were convinced that there had to be some underlying reason for my color palette. So a call was placed to my mother. In this call they asked my mom if I was sad at home, was acting differently, or if she had any ideas on how to expand my color choices. She replied with the truth, I was fine, I was happy, and most of all I was healthy. Well, that wasn't enough for the overly caring, no boundaries teachers. They removed every last one of the black and brown markers from the marker trays. From that day forward I never drew another picture on that easel.

It was not until I needed a title for my collection of poetry when my mother and I were brainstorming and she mentioned the black and brown marker incident at preschool. I laughed and said, "All the other markers were dried out and dirty – so I used the black and brown markers because they were clean and worked". We both laughed for a long time and I knew right then and there I had a title for my poetry collection.

Foreward

As more and more experiences occur in my life, I have only been able to form one solid conclusion...that it is not our experiences that connect us but the emotions that coincide with them. What I am trying to illustrate is that I could be living my life in one place, one town, one city, and you could be living yours somewhere completely different. Our lives could not be less similar, however we can always relate to each other through our emotions. We can all recognize sorrow, disbelief, and hope. I know every person has those and many more feelings inside of them, but I also know that I, like many others, have always had difficulty communicating them with everyone around me.

I hope that by reading my poetry everyone can allow their emotions to rise to the surface and allow themselves to recognize these emotions as the one common bond between us all. I have only allowed myself to accomplish this after years of trying to express myself through my writing and even now I am still unsure. I was only able to completely believe in my writing with the support and love of many people. But among those people a few have created a lasting impression on my heart.

My mother Laurie, my father Dean, and my sister Dana never doubt me, no matter what I choose to do. I realize that everyone is blessed with a limited number of people that love them unconditionally and I have been lucky enough to be supported by three of the most loving individuals in the world. When something goes wrong or does not go as I planned, they are always there to help me rebound back into me, and when I succeed at something, my mom, dad, and sister always make sure I know how proud of me they are. While writing the poems that went into this book they made me feel like the most talented writer in the world. I bounced all sorts of rough drafts and ideas off them, especially my mom (to the point where I would have found it extremely annoying), but they always supplied me with their honest opinions, thoughts, and constructive criticism. They have always loved and encouraged me and I know that they will continue to forever.

My doctors are really the reason that I am here and can share my emotions and experiences with everyone through my book. Whether they are the ones that know me like no one else, from the inside of my head out, or they helped me put all of the pieces back together after it was all said and done. I owe the deepest thanks in my heart to Dr. Sen, Dr. Costantino, Dr. Perin, and Dr. Allen. These gifted people have dedicated their lives to others and have taught me what life is really about and that when it is not possible to pay someone back, an even better way to show your gratitude is to pay it forward.

When a place of education feels more like a home than a school, you know you are somewhere special. The principal, Ms. Mahoney, assistant principals, guidance counselors, and teachers at Bridgewater Raritan Middle School have created that kind of remarkable environment for me over the past three years. There are teachers in your life that are not only your mentors but your friends and they give you the confidence and the encouragement to turn your thoughts into words. Mrs. Kym Weissenburger, or as I still call her Miss Matousek, has offered me her support. My writing would still be in a notebook, hidden in my room, if it was not for her guiding hand and undying support for me and my writing.

Every writer has a dream of sharing their writing with others. Thanks to the Marty Lyons Foundation, for me that dream has become a reality. Watching my book develop from the first drafts of the cover, to my words being printed at press time, it has been an experience like no other. I know that this great honor would not have been nearly the same if it was not for all of the caring and thoughtful people at the foundation that made sure all of my wishes came true.

As you read the poems written on the following pages I hope that you will stop to think past the words and connect your own thoughts and passions to them. The poems may have been created by me but in truth they are about each and every person in the world. After all, it is our feelings that we all have in common.

ADMIT
ONE
061807

As the Curtain Rises

Our future is an unsure thing
We're never certain of what tomorrow might bring
But, the experiences and friends from our past
Will all be members of our personal cast
The things we've learned and the people we've met
We've seen it all and now the stage is set
It's time to move forward, wait for our next cue
But, first a brief intermission, as we prepare for our debut
Some time to reflect, rehearse a few lines
Try out roles of all different kinds
Now the next act, the next year, our exposition is unclear
We move forward with conflicted hesitation
We compose pages of the script, our own creation
New experiences and relationships
Eternally illuminated as the spotlight hits
Cuts are made, lines we erase
Each elaborate scene moves at its own pace
The curtain drops, now it's only you
The lens is in focus for all critics to view
Take a deep breath, move center stage,
only you have the words to complete each page

Sometimes

Sometimes I'm a little different
Sometimes I'm a little strange
But no matter what I'm always open to a little change.
Sometimes I'm a little clumsy
Sometimes I'm a little confused
Sometimes when I'm with you I begin to feel a little used.
Sometimes I get frustrated
Sometimes I'm insane
Sometimes all my feelings burst like the cork on a bottle of champagne.
Sometimes I'm a little lost
Sometimes I don't know which way to turn
Sometimes I can't help it, but to my safe place return.
Sometimes I'm a little funny
Sometimes I'm a little dull
Sometimes my thoughts seem stuck in an ongoing lull.
Sometimes I don't know the difference
Sometimes I can't see
Sometimes I want to be left alone
Sometimes I just want to be me.

If You Believe

I'm me; it's what I was born to be
To follow my own dreams that are true to me
They flow through my head and stream through my heart
Nothing, no nothing can tear them apart

I'm me; it's what I was born to be
I have dreams, ambitions, and goals
Everyone does deep down in their souls

Everyone has a wish, a hope, a dream
They are unique despite how normal they may seem

The world is hard to keep up with
But if you focus on your goal
And reach deep down in your soul
You will achieve what ever you think,
If you only believe

I'm me; it's what I was born to be
I have a wish, a hope, a dream
I know I can reach them
If I just close my eyes and believe

Cast Out

What if you were cast out
Truly in your mind without a doubt
Who would you turn to if no one would talk to you
What would you do if that was true with everyone you knew
There was none that would offer to assist
No one to ask without the answer being no
Always the lingering question of where to go
Should you just turn away and accept the loneliness
But what about the companionship you will miss
For as long as you have yourself
You have everything you need
You have everything you need in order to be better than the greed
The greed that drives us to turn our backs
The same one that gives us the adrenaline to go forth on attack
It continues to push us no matter how badly we may bleed
Until those that we have cast out form a lengthy list
But it is that greed that we trust
It is only human to succeed to this feeling of lust
Instead, honor is where we place our doubt
But what if you were the one that was cast out
Truly in your mind with out a doubt

I Need to Know

I want to know about the people like me
Because now I know that we're not the same
I used to think that we were all one person
just going by two different names
I need to know where I belong
I need to know why I was built so strong
I need to know why I have been able to hold on for so long
Who are the other players in this game?
Are we all the same?
I need to know what they see when they look towards me
I need to know what I'm supposed to be
I need to know where I find the hidden key

I'm

And I'm leaping
And I'm flying
I can't touch the sky
But, still there are no boundaries that meet the eye
And I'm running
And I'm sliding
But, I can't stop myself as I hit the wall
And I'm waiting
And I'm placing a call
But there are just some times when everything seems as if it's fading
And sometimes I'm mad
And sometimes I just lose my head
But, the clear thoughts in my head come out mixed and jumbled instead
And sometimes I'm miserable
And sometimes I'm depressed
But, that's when my heart tells my mind it's time to protest
And sometimes I don't know
And sometimes I'm just not sure
But, no matter what, I'm sure that my emotions are always pure

Essence

There is a mystery of essence on placing your soul
beyond the human eye
So take a chance beyond your control
After all without decisions what really lies in your soul
So spread your wings and fly
Add another layer to your life for you never
Know when the spark in your soul may die
So take a step, a small one at that
Remember your past as you take a swing up at bat
For your past is what will lead you to your future deed
Take a chance, A chance to succeed
It's not something you have to do but something you may need
For there is a drive or longing for the unknown in all of us
So take one final chance and let your soul free to dance

Unseen

What if you knew of something?
Something you could not find
Something that could solve your troubles and ease your mind
How far would you be willing to search?
What distance would you travel?
Just how many paths would you be willing to follow?
Would you leave no stone unturned?
Would you do it all with fervor, leaving no bridge unburned?
Would you walk until you reached the end?
Would you gaze over the ridge?
What if you searched through all the Seven Wonders?
From the depths of the oceans and caverns below
To the glowing horizon and mountain peaks covered in glistening snow
What if this search you had to extend
What if this something wasn't hidden in an actual place?
At least not one you could look at face to face
What if this something was inside a person?
What if it caused you to look deep into someone's eyes?
And to their outer shell pay no mind?
For it's on the inside that we are wise
It's appearances that cause us to lose the true meaning of the words people say
Imagine the knowledge and wisdom that could be shared
if the whole world was blind
A whole new moral the world would convey
If only we would stop to look inside someone new each day
To solve your troubles and ease your mind
You have to go on a search of a different kind
Not one with a set destination
But one within others different from you
Then you will arrive at something: Inspiration

A Spark is a Seed

Hope is the spark in your heart
That has the power to carry you away
It is one of the few things that can lead you in a new direction each day
If you travel in the direction that it leads
From a spark into a fire it may bleed
For a little believing is all that is in need
But, in a different light that spark is like a seed
With just a few demands to grow into a tree
Just a few things needed to succeed
So take care and kindle your spark
For if it goes out there will be nothing but dark
The hope sparks your dreams
Until from within you the hope, light, and dreams beam
So make sure to help it grow
Until like a wildfire the hope may flow
Hope is the spark in your heart
It is the place were everything forms a start

What They Think

I know what everyone says about you
Do you?

Do you care?
Does it have an impact on you when they stare?

I know what they say when you walk away
But it never sticks with you till the next day

Do you have the strength?
The strength to not let what they say rip away
Rip at your soul
Rip and tear each day

I wouldn't, but you do
I don't think you would if you only knew

Would you let them change you?
Would you try to be like them with everything you say and do?

Do you have the courage to stay true?
Stay true to you
Stay among the few

I wouldn't but you do
I don't think you would if only you knew
If only you knew what they say and do

Tell Me a Story...

Tell me a story from when you were young
What books did you read, what songs have you sung?
What do you remember?
Anything from the end of December or May maybe mid-September?
Tell me about life in 1960 something
To what moments does your memory still cling?
Will you share them with me?
I want to know what it was like
What did you do after school?
Did you go to the candy shop on the corner,
or did you travel around town on a bike?
Did you ever do something you weren't supposed to?
Did you ever break even one single rule?
Tell me a story from a time in the past
I want to know about where you lived,
I want to know about where you grew
I want to know everything, from when it all started
to what you did last

I'm beginning to fall asleep
But promise that you won't stop
For now I'll sleep through the night with dreams of you and I
in the corner candy shop

Only You

And sometimes I'm not sure what to do
And sometimes I'm not certain where to turn
When everything around me seems to crash and burn
My life goes up in flames
And I'm stuck inside with no one to call out to, not a single name
But then I take a short breath, and all I can think of is you
Will you remember that I love you
Will you remember that I care
Will you remember that no matter what I will always be there
And then the flames enclose
And the embers continually burn
Have I finally worked hard enough for your love also to earn
Have you finally realized that that is for what I truly yearn
And then the smoke begins to fill me
And the pain begins to set in
Will you recognize my cry, will you acknowledge my concluding plea
Will you finally pay the attention I feel is deserved to me

Underneath the Surface

Never ending, Always there, Never happy, Always scared
Thoughts of every single kind, twisted and mangled inside my mind
Always leering out of sight, yet never clearer than at night
Haunting, Shadowing, Twisting around,
Thoughts clearly never confound
Never latent, Always waiting, Never testing, Always doubting
Whittled and labeled; intertwined, forever embedded in my mind
Always lurking out of reach, and yet the pain is so evident
Needling like a prickling leech
Never mending, Always condescending, Never healing
Always pending, Never consistent, Always shifting
The emotions in thoughts behind them eerily pulse and glow
Hate, Sorrow, and Fury; any that you know
They are black and solemn with an oily flow
Always gathering, Never departing, Always leaking through the cracks
Slipping undetected with their ceaseless attacks
It does not matter where the thoughts reside
When they're all adversaries inside my mind
They never cease to swirl and swish
A moment of peace is all that I wish
Thoughts that never take a moment to rest
They cause the constant shaking and pounding inside my chest
And yet if they weren't there, Never ending and Always scaring
I doubt that I could handle what I might find
Lying so peacefully inside my mind

Something

The world around you twists and turns
The fire and light forever burns
Unyielding and painful, unwilling to concede
Forever leaving you with a longing need
Unyielding torture or unforgiving pain
No matter what you call it, it hurts just the same
Yearning for darkness to rest your eyes
Or maybe just a little shade
You're always willing to compromise
The light seems to cut through your heart like a sharpened blade
Searching for someone, something to come to your aid

The Life in Your Shadow

The shadow that walks beside you
It is not the shadow of just you
It is the shadow of someone you loved too
Your shadow is with you always
Even the times you cannot see it throughout the days

The sun that shines upon you
It is not just the sun to you
It is the warmness of love wrapping around you
In it lays the soul of a loved one
Splashing down upon you

As you stare into the blank sky
To see the strong hawk flying high
A single hawk, the sign of courage and bravery
Know that is a sign of a loved one's presence that you see
Know that the special one's presence will never flee

The bunny that hops by, then stops to observe blankly
It sits and stares silently almost saintly
But if you stop to look close deep down its eyes
You will find that there is a part of it you recognize
The sparkle is the same as someone you know
Now you will know that their soul is always in tow

The family of birds that is chirping a song up in the towering tree
It opens your heart like a lock and the key
But if you listen closely you will find
The something remembered in your soul and in your mind
For the song they are singing is the one of life, the life of someone you loved
You know all the pitches, the twists and turns
For in that song part of you burns

Your shadow and everything that walks beside you is the sign of love
It is as soft and pure as a gliding dove

Everyday

Everyday a new chance arrives
Everyday a new problem appears
But everyday we continue, believing without fear
Hope just revives
Fear is just a glimpse
Someday we will complete our forgotten promise
Our promise to see one another without a lasting rawness
Sight is just a message
Hope is just a fear
Nothing in between matters
When all of them are near
Everyday happiness occurs
Everyday sadness sets in
But everyday we continue loving
Loving without doubt
Love is just a feeling
Feelings are just a hope
Feeling love is simply a certain form of healing
Healing from the inside out
Everyday a new chance arrives
Everyday a new problem appears
But everyday we continue, believing without fear
Hope just revives
Fear is just a glimpse
Hope and fear engrave
But yet everyday all together they save

Apologies

I'm sorry for the things that have been said
I'm sorry for everything that's been done
I am sorry for some of the choices I have made
But I am not sorry in the least come the end
It has all turned out okay
If I had done it differently who knows where I may be sitting today
I am sorry for the consequence
I am sorry that at the time, to you, it made no sense
I am sorry for some of the things I have said
But I am not sorry in the least come the end
It has all turned out just fine
If I hadn't done what I've done who knows what today I could call mine
I am sorry I didn't include you in all of my decisions
I am sorry that in order to understand the impact
you must experience the collision
I am sorry that I'm not perfect
I am sorry that I'm not everything you expect me to be
I am not sorry that I am what I choose to see
I am not sorry that everything didn't work out as planned
I am sorry that our ship couldn't anchor before it crashed on land
I am sorry that I can't make up for what I've missed
I am sorry that through it all I pretended the tension didn't exist
Then maybe all of this could have been evaded
For now lets leave it be, all paths have been blockaded

Amending the View

What if the world stopped spinning
What would happen to all of the dreams,
The dreams of the young, the weak, and the frail?
The ones whose thoughts and passions only at night get to sail
Would hope simply rip at the seams, could life possibly carry on
Would we all stumble around as does a helpless fawn,
Young and naive with no one to turn to?
Serenity in our eyes, but fire within our hearts
From the flame could we capture a spark,
And kindle that ember until it brands a mark?
The joyous and the dreadful must both be experienced
A world that you must look inside yourself to construct,
For that is the source where the strength comes from.
Like a bleeding sunset could we unite
The reds, yellows, and purples reflecting the armor of an avenging knight
Our diversity bonding all together, could our passion remain devout?
Could we unite among the fury
Or would unreasonable doubt arise throughout the jury
Could we all possibly shout in one rising voice.
Or in millions of directions would we scatter with a single choice?
Would the population split along a fragile fault line
Would we all continue on ignoring the road sign
For the opinions of people that appear so different, are really quite the same
A character merely called by a different name
Would the ocean continue flowing
Could the world proceed without anyone even knowing
For if the world stopped for me, would it be the end for you,
Or simply the beginning of something new?

A Look

And then I began to wonder is it me
Or is it the broken image that they all see
But no matter what view we are peering through
It is still my mind, body, and soul
Things that are always under my control
But the only view that truly counts is my view from the inside out
What the world chooses to see is out of my command
Could it be that what they see when they look at me
Is really a combination of what they hate in themselves
Things they have tried to ignore by stowing them on dusty shelves
The gaze from their eyes
The lingering glare
Is it all simply a poorly placed disguise
Have we all finally reached a moment of despair?

Hand in Hand

Take my hand and promise not to let go
As long as I feel you there, I know everything will be okay
With your hand in mine I can defeat even the toughest foe
With your hand in my mine I will never again reach despair
Fingertip to fingertip your daring power now also flows through me
Thanks to you I now too believe I can become whatever I want to be
With you pushing me on I can accomplish whatever I want to
Due to you I now see myself in a positive view
I see myself conquering mountains and calming winds
I see myself exploring the ocean as if I had fins
I'm beginning to slip so make your grip a little tighter
With your hand in mine I know I can be a fighter
With your hand in mine my future always looks a little brighter

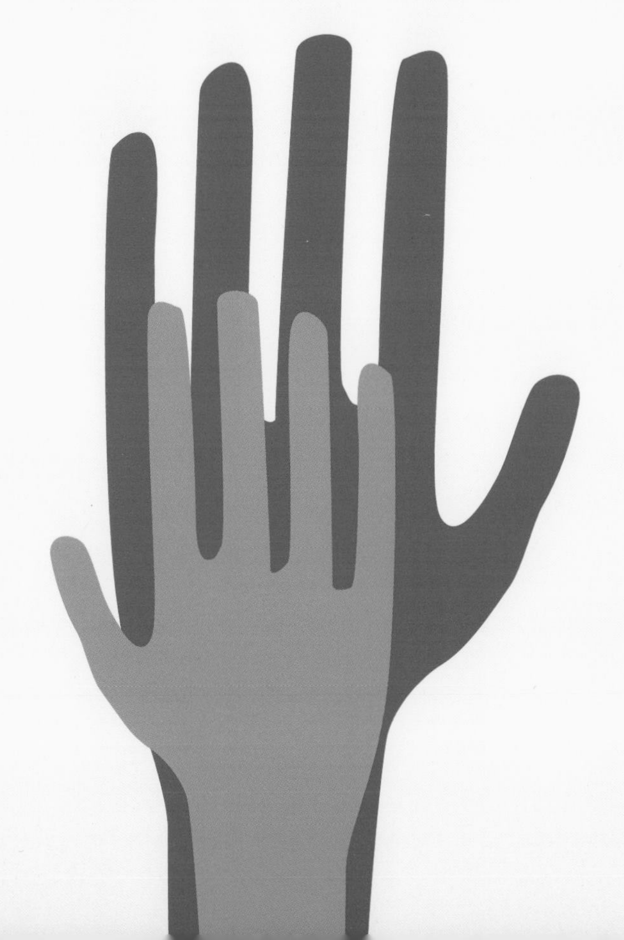

Tears

Do the tears flow just for someone you know?
Or do you also feel the sorrow for someone you may have met tomorrow
Even though you didn't get the chance
Do you still try to dance

Do you cry?
About something you failed at
But at least you can say you tried
Would you rather never fail
But then you would never have experienced the joy of feeling the wind
as it blows through your sail

Do you tear at the sudden hint of sadness?
But then again what will those tears cause you to miss
The experience of your life or just something cutting through
your heart like a knife

Do you keep the sadness inside of you?
Are you afraid to say, but then what can you do
Will it weigh you down forever
Or will you stay light until you can say never

Do you cry for yourself?
When you're sad or you feel small
Do you let yourself keep tumbling after you take the first fall
Do you deny the right to feel bad for yourself
Do you feel it's just not worth it
Or are you held together with the entangled feelings you knit

Do the tears flow just for someone you know?
Do you cry
Do you tear at the sudden hint of sadness
Do you keep the sadness inside of you
Do you cry for yourself

The choice is up to you
They're your feelings, but it's your life too

Pieces of Life

What would you do if you thought
You had put your life back together again
Then in an instant it disintegrated apart
Life leaves you completely lost, nowhere to even start
Where do you begin to rebuild
Is there any reason to even start, for all your dreams have been killed?
Even if you made it all the way to the top
Would it last?

For from the top there is an even bigger drop
What would you do if life left you lost?
Would you realign the pieces no matter what the cost?
What pain and disappointment might come?
The pain and disappointment that comes when all your effort has been lost

What if your life took off?
But at an even bigger cost
Would it be worth it to lose everything?
Some might say yes
But then you have to rebuild once again
Perhaps if you lay down your dreams in iron pen
Only then everything can you fully comprehend
Then you will no longer be left to guess

With You

As I look into your eyes
All my fears and insecurities die
Suddenly I have the strength to overcome the lies
I have the strength to deify
As I fall into your arms
The blaring of my mind's alarms
Fall silent
I no longer need to simply comply
I can do what I feel is right
There is no need for me to hide my feelings in the darkness of night
With you my true thoughts can finally take flight

How Can You Tell Me

How can you tell me that it's not worth my tears?
It's all I've waited for, for all of these years
How can you look me in the eye and tell me that these feelings will die?
It's everything I've worked for, hour after hour
How can you listen to me and my thoughts not empower?
It's what I've looked towards, day to day
How can you know me and not know that now
the yearning in my heart has gone astray?
It's what I've put my love into week after week
How can you sit there and my ambitions critique?
It's what I've traveled towards, mile after mile
How can you answer me with opinions so hostile?
It's what I thought I knew
It's what with persistence I thought I should pursue
But now with your opinions to consider I'm not certain what to do

Dream Maker

Someone to believe in you
Have faith in everything you say and do
Someone to have a constant smile
Even if the distance between you is further than a colossal mile
To be there any time of day
To listen to everything you have to say
To offer support
And through all your problems help you sort
To share opinions, old and new
Thoughts that always seem to get you through
Someone to show you love
Something with them there is never a shortage of
Someone who's voice brings a smile to your face
A voice that always brings a caring embrace
An angel that always flies overhead
With plenty of love to spread
A fairy godmother
Someone like no other

The Smile in Your Gaze

A hidden smile
A silent gaze
These feelings inside, like a winding maze
We just keep wandering mile for mile; led by only a hidden smile
Which way to turn
Which way to go
With each direction change, there's something to learn
A wrong turn here, some misdirection there
Nothing, however to lead us to total despair
We'll get where we're going, of this I'm sure
When we have each other there's nothing we can't endure

The Joy You Share

Tears you cry, joy you share
Those who love you truly care
When times are rough or even smooth
They are always there to help you through

The time you spend with these special few
Are the moments that mean the most to you
Memories left in our heart
For the rest of your life, this is the start

Happiness and joy is what they bring
They add to your life with the song they sing
They enrich your life until you live like a king

In all the moments you've shared
Have they ever truly cared
Have they ever really dared

In truth the answer is quite simple
But don't look inside of them for all you will see is you
You have to look inside of yourself for then you see them too

This may not fit the time now
But if you give it some time you will see
The answer doesn't lie in you or I, but we

Tears you cry, joy you share
Those who love you truly care
When times are rough or even smooth
They are always there to help you through

The time you spend with these special few
Are the moments that mean the most to you
Memories left in your heart
For the rest of your life, this is the start
Together you can fit the part

Standing in the Spotlight

The light nears
As the audience appears
And the crowd begins to cheer

Swirling through a world
The perfect world
Where all the stories are twirled and the plots are curled

Like a chameleon
You must change your skin to fit the part
Soon you will not be able to tell
Yourself and the character apart
That is when it becomes true art

The lights begin to dim
As the audience appears
And the crowd begins to cheer

For if you are made to standout
You have to believe, not doubt

You move forward to take your bow
And you are great right then, right now

This is the life we live in,
You are never truly free to be yourself until
you feel that sense of accomplishment
It is a feeling deep down inside, one that only comes with
the feeling of pride
For that is when you stop acting and become who you want to be
That is when you and everyone truly see